Babyfather

by

Joanna Kenrick

Based on the gr8read novel *Babyfather*
by Joanna Kenrick

K oR
A432873

First published in 2009 in Great Britain by
Barrington Stoke Ltd
18 Walker St, Edinburgh, EH3 7LP

www.barringtonstoke.co.uk

ISBN: 978-1-84299-645-4

Printed in Great Britain by Bell & Bain Ltd

Introduction

In the story *Babyfather*, Mickey finds out his girlfriend Emma is pregnant. Like a lot of boys, Mickey doesn't say how he really feels. In a book, you can show what he's thinking, but that's not so easy in a play. I was worried that people might think Mickey doesn't care, so that's why he often talks to the audience. It's so that they can understand what he's really thinking and how he really feels.

There are lots of books about teenagers getting pregnant. But most of them are all about the girl – how she feels. I wrote *Babyfather* because I wanted people to think about how the boy might feel, and how hard it is for him to know what to do.

For Laura Butcher, an unsung heroine

Contents

Cast

Mickey

Mickey is 15 years old. He is easy-going and likes a laugh. He lives with his mum and most of the time he gets on with everyone.

Emma

Emma has been Mickey's girlfriend for the last few months. She's cool. Like Mickey, she has an easy-going outlook on life.

Josh

Josh is Mickey's best friend. He likes a good time but he cares most about his image. He thinks he's good-looking enough to be a model when he leaves school.

Sophie

Sophie is in the same year at school as Mickey and Emma. She always says what she thinks, even if people don't want to hear it.

Cathy

Cathy is Sophie's friend at school. They go around everywhere together and love to gossip.

Miss Dobson

Miss Dobson is the school counsellor. The students call her "Old Dobby". She has wispy hair and glasses. She thinks she is good at her job, but no one likes talking to her.

Aunt Kelly

Aunt Kelly is Mickey's aunt. She's a cool sort of person and really easy to talk to. She would always stand up for Mickey, but she isn't afraid to tell him when he's doing something wrong.

Scene 1

Mickey's Bedroom

Mickey's bedroom is a mess. There are clothes all over the floor. There is a chair in the corner with books, football stuff and magazines in a pile on top of it. There are posters on the walls.

(Mickey is in bed, asleep. His mobile rings. Mickey wakes up, puts out his arm, and feels around for the phone. When he finds it, he sits up to answer it, still half asleep.)

Mickey: Hello?

(It's Emma's voice on the phone.)

Emma:	It's me.
Mickey:	Emma? Jeez, what's the time?
Emma:	I don't know.
Mickey:	You OK?
Emma:	No, I'm not. Mickey, I ... can we talk?

(Mickey looks at the audience and rolls his eyes.)

Mickey:	Course. What about?
Emma:	Not on the phone. I need to see you.

Mickey: You'll see me at school in
                about …

(Mickey checks his clock.)

Mickey: … two hours.

Emma: This can't wait. Can I come
                over now?

Mickey: Now? Uh – yeah, I guess.

*(Mickey sits up quickly and starts looking
around for some clothes.)*

Emma: OK. See you in a minute.

(Mickey hangs up the phone. He starts getting dressed for school. He turns and talks to the audience.)

Mickey: Oh, God, she said it. Those three little words. "Can we talk?" The girlfriend words of doom. It's never anything good, is it? It's never how much the girl likes me, or what a sweet guy I am. Oh, no. Those words mean they want to moan about something. Like how I don't understand how they feel. Or I forgot their birthday. And if it's not that, it's the start of the other thing – the breaking-up speech. Like "It's not you, it's me," which really means, "It is you, but I'm a wimp, so I'm not going to say it." Where's my tie? Oh – there it is. So here we go again. I thought things were going pretty well with Emma. She's a cool sort of girl – doesn't get all worked up over stupid stuff. We've been going out for ... I can't remember. A few months, I guess. But it sounds like I've done something wrong now.

Oh, God – it wasn't her
birthday, was it?

(There is a knock at the bedroom door and Emma comes in.)

Mickey: Hi.

Emma: Hi.

(Mickey and Emma stand looking at each other. At first, they don't say anything. Then both of them start talking at the same time.)

Mickey: Did you want to sit down?

Emma: I've got something to tell you.

(They stop talking and look at each other again.)

Mickey: Sorry, after you.

Emma: I don't know how to say this. So I'm just going to come out with it.

(Mickey is feeling nervous.)

Mickey: OK.

Emma: I'm pregnant.

(Mickey looks shocked. Then he thinks Emma must be joking, and laughs.)

Mickey:	Way to give a bloke a heart attack, Emma!

(Emma bursts into tears.)

Mickey:	Oh, man. Look – come and sit down.

(Mickey takes Emma over to the bed and sits down next to her.)

Mickey:	Do you need a tissue? Hang on, I've got a box somewhere.

(Mickey jumps up and goes over to the chair. Then he starts picking things up, looking for a box of tissues.)

Emma: What are you doing? Didn't
               you hear me? I'm pregnant!

Mickey: They're under here, I
               think ...

Emma: Mickey!

(Mickey stops looking and stands still. He
turns to Emma.)

Mickey: Yeah, OK. I heard you. I just
               – I mean – well, how come?

Emma: How do you think? Don't you
               go to biology lessons with
               the rest of us?

Mickey:	Yeah, of course. But we've only – you know – done it once.
Emma:	It only takes once.
Mickey:	You told me it was your first time.
Emma:	It was!
Mickey:	I thought you couldn't get pregnant the first time.
Emma:	Well, you were wrong.
Mickey:	Why didn't you go on the Pill?

Emma:	Oh, so now it's my fault!
Mickey:	No, I'm not saying that …
Emma:	Why didn't *you* use a condom?
Mickey:	I didn't have any.

(Mickey and Emma both stop talking. Mickey looks at the chair. Emma looks at the floor.)

Mickey:	What are you going to do?
Emma:	What do you mean?
Mickey:	Well – are you going to keep it?

(Emma is shocked.)

Emma: You think I should get rid of it!

Mickey: If you don't want it.

Emma: If *I* don't want it? Oh, thanks, so I get to choose all on my own, do I?

Mickey: You're the one who's pregnant.

Emma: And you're the one that got me in this state! I'm only fifteen, Mickey.

Mickey: So am I!

(Emma starts crying again.)

Emma: What are we going to do?

(Mickey sits down on the bed and puts his arm around Emma.)

Mickey: Don't cry.

(Emma pushes Mickey away and stands up.)

Emma: Don't touch me. I can't
                 think. I – I need to go. I'll
                 call you.

(Emma turns and walks out of Mickey's bedroom. Sitting on his own now, he looks up and speaks to the audience.)

Mickey: OK. So that turned out

                worse than I thought.

Scene 2

Outside the School Gates

It is an hour later. Josh, Mickey's friend, is waiting for him outside the school gates. Through the gates you can see a school playground and a large building. Students are going in through the gates, pushing and laughing.

(Josh is standing to one side, trying to look cool. He checks his hair in the shiny buckle on his bag. Mickey comes in, walking slowly and looking at the ground.)

Mickey: Hey, Josh.

Josh:	Hey, Mickey. So is it true you got Emma up the duff?
Mickey:	Jeez, bad news travels fast. Who told you?
Josh:	Emma told Cathy, who told Pari, who told Olly, who told me.
Mickey:	God.
Josh:	So it's true, then?
Mickey:	Yeah, I guess. Well, she wouldn't lie, would she? Not about something like that.

Josh: Are you sure it's yours,
          mate?

Mickey: What do you mean?

Josh: You know what girls are like.
          How do you know it's yours?

Mickey: Are you calling Emma a
          slag?

Josh: No, mate, course not. Don't
          stress. Just saying you can't
          trust them sometimes.

Mickey: Well, I trust Emma. Besides,
          I was her first. You know –
          her first time.

Josh: So she says.

Mickey: And I believe her, all right?
                 You want to make something
                 of it?

Josh: No, no, whatever you say. So
                 what's she going to do about
                 it?

Mickey: That's what I asked. But she
                 went all weird on me. Said
                 she couldn't choose on her
                 own. She kept asking *me*
                 what she should do.

Josh: But she's the one who's
                 pregnant, not you.

21

Mickey: That's what I said! Then she
started crying.

Josh: Girls. What planet are they
on?

(Sophie and Cathy, two girls in the same year as Mickey, walk by. When they see Mickey, they give him angry looks.)

Sophie: You git.

Mickey: Huh?

Cathy: How could you be so stupid?

Mickey: What?

Sophie: Poor Emma.

Mickey: Um …

Cathy: I hope you're going to do the
                 right thing.

Mickey: What right thing?

*(Sophie and Cathy just look at Mickey. They
raise their eyebrows at him.)*

Josh: So, I'll be off now, then …

(Josh walks off, hoping no one will see him.)

Sophie: Come on, Cathy. He's a
                 waste of space.

Cathy: Yeah. What did Emma ever
                 see in him anyway?

Sophie: God knows.

(Cathy and Sophie walk away. Mickey, left on his own now, turns to the audience.)

Mickey: "Do the right thing"? What are they talking about? Oh, God, please no – they can't mean I should ask Emma to marry me. Can they? I'm not ready to get married. Not for years and years. Anyway, I don't love Emma. Hang on, that makes me sound really mean. I like Emma – I like her a lot. I

went to bed with her, didn't
I? But marry her? No way!

(Mickey lets out a long sigh.)

Mickey: Could things get any worse?

(Josh comes back out to see Mickey.)

Josh: Mate, I hate to tell you, but
the counsellor wants to see
you.

(Mickey is still talking to the audience.)

Mickey: Of course they could.

Scene 3

Miss Dobson's Office

Miss Dobson, the school counsellor, is sitting at her desk. There is a rack of trays on one side, with paper spilling out of it. On the desk, in front of Miss Dobson, is a brown folder with Mickey's name on it and a pot of pens. In front of the desk is a chair.

(There is a knock at the door and Mickey comes in.)

Mickey: Miss Dobson? You wanted to see me?

Miss Dobson:	Ah, Michael. Sit down, please. You must know why you're here.
Mickey:	Well ...
Miss Dobson:	I've been talking to Emma.
Mickey:	Oh.
Miss Dobson:	And I think we need to talk too – you and me.
Mickey:	OK. Talk all you want.
Miss Dobson:	You do understand that this is important, don't you?

Mickey: Of course I do. I'm not
                 stupid.

Miss Dobson: She's going to have a baby.

Mickey: I know. She'll have to leave
                 school. No going to college,
                 blah blah. Important. I get
                 it.

Miss Dobson: It's not just important for
                 her. It's important for you
                 too.

Mickey: I don't see why.

Miss Dobson: Because no matter what you
                 think, the two of you are in

this together. You're going
to be a father.

(Mickey sits back and can't help laughing.)

Mickey: That's just so weird.

Miss Dobson: It's not funny, Michael.
                    You're going to have to grow
                    up very fast.

Mickey: I am grown-up.

Miss Dobson: Well, you're not behaving
                    that way.

(Mickey rolls his eyes.)

Miss Dobson: Don't roll your eyes at me, young man. You've got important things to think about now. It's not all about you any more. You've got Emma and the baby too. It's time for you to face facts. But I can see you don't want to hear what I've got to say, so I won't waste my breath.

(Mickey turns and speaks to the audience.)

Mickey: Thank God for that.

Miss Dobson:	You need to talk to Emma.
Mickey:	She doesn't want to talk to me.
Miss Dobson:	Well, Michael, that doesn't surprise me. You've only got yourself to blame. Stop thinking about yourself for once. You owe it to Emma.

(Mickey stands up.)

Mickey:	Thanks, Miss Dobson. You've really helped me see things more clearly – not!

Miss Dobson: I can't help if you won't listen. Maybe you'll listen to someone else.

(As Mickey walks out of the room, Miss Dobson picks up the phone.)

Scene 4

Outside the School Gates

It's the end of the school day. Students are coming out of school to go home.

(Mickey and Josh are walking together, carrying their school bags.)

Josh: So what did Old Dobby the counsellor say?

Mickey: I should grow up, stop being selfish, blah blah. The same old stuff. And talk to Emma again.

Josh: Are you going to?

Mickey: How can I? Look …

(Mickey pulls out his mobile and presses speed dial for Emma's number. He waits for it to connect and then holds the mobile to Josh's ear.)

Mickey: See? Voicemail. She knows it's me. I've left a message but she hasn't called back. She's mad at me.

Josh: So what now?

Mickey: God knows. There's nothing I can do.

Josh:	We should go out tonight. Have a good time. Forget all this crap.
Mickey:	Yeah, you're right. I could do with a good night out.

(Mickey's mobile beeps and he reads the text message.)

Mickey:	Oh, that's all I need.
Josh:	What is it?
Mickey:	My mum knows. I am in so much trouble.

Josh:	So much for going out tonight.
Mickey:	Yeah. No chance now.
Josh:	We could just go into town anyway ...
Mickey:	No. It'll be worse if I put it off. I've got to go home and face the music.
Josh:	Good luck, mate. You're going to need it.

Scene 5

Mickey's House

The front door to Mickey's house leads into the front room, which has a sofa and small coffee table. There are two mugs of tea on the table. There is a TV in one corner and another door leading to the kitchen.

(Mickey is standing outside his front door, holding his key in his hand. He turns and speaks to the audience.)

Mickey: I don't want to go in. Mum will blow my head off, I just know it. She's gonna kill me. She got pregnant with me when she was sixteen. She never stops going on about it. How she never got the breaks in life. Of course she loves me, but if she had the chance to go back, she would never have had a baby. Not then. She says no one knows what it's like unless they've been through it. And she wants me to go to college and everything. Do the stuff she never did. But now it looks like I'll be doing the same as her. She's gonna hit the roof. Oh well, here goes.

(Mickey moves to put his key in the lock, but the door is opened by Aunt Kelly.)

Mickey: Aunt Kelly! What are you doing here?

Aunt Kelly: Oh, that's a nice welcome, that is. And hello to you too!

Mickey: Sorry. I'm just glad it's you. Where's Mum?

Aunt Kelly: In the back. She wants me to talk to you first.

Mickey: Oh. I guess you've heard, then.

| Aunt Kelly: | Yeah. You've got yourself in a bit of a mess, haven't you? |

(Mickey tries to laugh but it isn't really funny.)

| Mickey: | Looks like it. |

| Aunt Kelly: | I've made a cup of tea. Come and sit down. |

(Mickey and Aunt Kelly walk over to the sofa and sit down.)

| Mickey: | Is Mum really mad? |

| Aunt Kelly: | Oh, you know. She's just sad that things have turned out this way for you. But this |

	isn't about her. How are you holding up?
Mickey:	Dunno. It's weird. Everyone's angry – Emma, her mates, the school counsellor.
Aunt Kelly:	Are they wrong to be angry?
Mickey:	It wasn't my fault. How was I to know she'd get pregnant?

(Aunt Kelly raises her eyebrows at Mickey.)

Mickey:	OK, OK. Maybe I was a bit stupid. But what's the point

in yelling at me now? I can't do anything about it.

Aunt Kelly: I agree. It's too late for blame now. You have to think of the future.

Mickey: That's too scary.

Aunt Kelly: Bad luck, you don't have any choice. Is Emma going to keep the baby?

Mickey: I don't know. She started talking about it but she kept crying. Then she just walked off.

Aunt Kelly: She's scared. Really scared. Even more than you.

Mickey: I guess.

Aunt Kelly: Being pregnant is a big thing for a girl. It changes everything. She'll feel another person growing inside of her. That's a massive thing – it takes over your mind and body and you have no control. She's got the labour and birth to think about, and that can be really scary. Plus, when the baby comes, she's got to look after it *all* the time. You two aren't married and I don't suppose you will be.

Mickey: No way!

Aunt Kelly: So she doesn't know for sure if you'll even be around. That means she's got to do everything herself – all the looking after. The first few months are the hardest. She won't sleep for more than three hours at a time. She'll be so tired. The baby will cry and shit because that's what babies do. But worst of all, she'll know she can't ever be free again. Can't ever just go out with her mates, whenever she feels like it. The baby will always come first.

Mickey: Jeez, Aunt Kelly. Are you trying to make me feel even worse?

Aunt Kelly: Sorry, Mickey. I know you're scared too. I'm just trying to show you that this is a big thing. Bringing up a baby is so hard. It's even harder when you're doing it on your own.

Mickey:	What are you trying to say?
Aunt Kelly:	I know you didn't plan this. And I'm guessing that if you had the chance again you'd do things differently.
Mickey:	Too right.
Aunt Kelly:	But you know what? You can make the best of this, Mickey. It's going to be hard, but you can do it.

Mickey: Do what?

Aunt Kelly: Be there for them. For
Emma and the baby. Your
child. You can be a dad.

Mickey: A dad ... me?

Aunt Kelly: You. You can support Emma
in whatever she chooses to
do.

(Aunt Kelly passes Mickey the phone.)

Aunt Kelly: And you can start by calling
her right now.

Mickey: She won't talk to me.

Aunt Kelly: Keep trying.

(Aunt Kelly stands up and leaves the room.)

Scene 6

Mickey's House

(Mickey is sitting on the sofa, looking at the phone in his hand. He takes a deep breath and dials.)

Mickey: Hi – can I speak to Emma?
           It's Mickey ... Yes, I know. I –
           I'm sorry. I really need to
           talk to her. Please ... Emma?
           It's me. I need to talk to
           you. Can I come round? ...
           Oh, I see. Well, can you
           come here, then? I just – I
           think we should talk
           face-to-face, don't you? OK.

Yeah. See you in a minute,
then.

*(Mickey hangs up the phone. He stands up
and speaks to the audience.)*

Mickey: Jeez. What am I going to

say? Aunt Kelly talks sense,

but still ... What if I'm crap

at this? I don't know how to

be a dad! I don't want to be

tied down for the rest of my

life. What if Emma makes

me pay loads of money for

the baby – where am I going

to get it from? Mum's

always going on about how

we have no money anyway. I'd have to get a job. But what about school? I have to get some exams, don't I?

(Mickey sits down.)

Mickey: How did things go so wrong? I didn't think she would get pregnant – I didn't think at all. And now everything's gone to hell. And all of a sudden I have to be grown-up. It's too bloody scary. Aunt Kelly thinks I can do it. She's a cool sort of lady. But what if she's wrong?

(The front door-bell rings.)

Mickey: Oh, God. I'm not ready.
                     What the hell am I going to
                     say? Come on, Mickey. You
                     can do this.

(Mickey opens the door. Emma is standing outside.)

Mickey: Hi Emma. You … look good.

Emma: Is that all you've got to say?

Mickey: No – no! I'm sorry. I don't
                     know how to do this.

Emma: Nor do I.

Mickey:	Come in. Sit down. Do you want a drink?
Emma:	No, thanks.

(Mickey and Emma sit down on the sofa.)

Mickey:	I'm sorry.
Emma:	You said that.
Mickey:	Yeah, but I really mean it. I've been talking to my aunt and she made me understand some stuff.
Emma:	Like what?

Mickey:	Like how this should be something we face together. You shouldn't be on your own. Whatever you choose to do. Whatever *we* choose to do.
Emma:	Go on.
Mickey:	I mean, in the end it's your body. So I don't want to make you do anything if it's not what you want. If you don't want to keep the baby, then I'll make sure you're OK. I'll be there for you – you can talk to me any time.

Emma: And if I do keep the baby?

Mickey: Then I'll still be there for you. For both of you.

Emma: How do you mean?

Mickey: I'll get a job. Do my exams and then make sure I get a good job. To get enough money for all three of us. Babies are expensive – nappies and stuff.

Emma: It's not just the money, Mickey.

Mickey:	I know. I'll help out in other ways too. Take it to the park so you get a break. Teach it to play football.
Emma:	What if it's a girl?
Mickey:	Hey, I'm not sexist. She'll still play football. And she'll support West Ham. Or else.

(Emma laughs. Then she looks worried again.)

Emma:	It's not all going to be fun, you know.

Mickey:	I know. But I'm going to help. Do my bit. Like family.
Emma:	Are you going soft on me, Mickey Evans?
Mickey:	No way! I'm being a man, that's all. Men look after their women.
Emma:	Now you're being an arse.
Mickey:	Made you smile, though.

(Emma smiles, even though she's trying not to.)

Emma: Did not.

Mickey: Don't get rid of it, Em. I
               really mean that. Please
               don't.

Emma: I did think about it. My
               mum wants me to. But I
               don't think I could, Mickey.
               Not get rid of my baby.

Mickey: Our baby.

Emma: You really mean all that?
               About helping out and
               everything?

| Mickey: | Course I do. I said, didn't I? Anyhow, my mum and aunt are big on keeping promises. I'd never hear the end of it if I let you down. |

(Emma smiles at Mickey.)

| Emma: | I suddenly remember why I like you. |

| Mickey: | Because I'm well fit, that's why. |

| Emma: | No, it's because, inside, you're a really nice guy. |

Mickey: Not so loud! People might

               hear you!

(Emma laughs.)

Emma: Too late, your secret's out.

               Mickey the charmer ...

(Emma takes Mickey's hand and puts it on
her stomach.)

Emma: ... Say hi to your baby.

               You're going to be a dad.

Mickey: Holy crap.

Emma: I know. But it'll be OK. We

             can do it.

Mickey: We can do it.

**Perfect: The Play
by
Joanna Kenrick**

Too good to be true?
Dan and Kate are
perfect together.
Nothing can go wrong.
Until the lying starts.

**Mind-Set: The Play
by
Joanna Kenrick**

Mark and Shaleem are
best mates.
But the bombs change
everything.
Will Mark stand up for
Shaleem when it
matters?

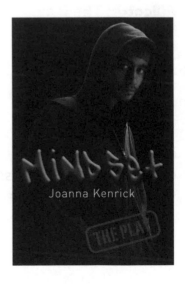

You can order these books directly from our website at
www.barringtonstoke.co.uk

Thing: The Play
by
Chris Powling

Black button eyes.
Ziz-zag mouth.
Stiff body.
Thing.

Once it was Robbie's
best friend. Now it's
become his enemy ...

Alligator: The Play
by
Theresa Breslin and
Julie Gormley

Jono has a problem.
He's just got himself an
alligator. His mum is
going to kill him. Unless
the alligator gets there
first.

You can order these books directly from our website at
www.barringtonstoke.co.uk